Stop Taking My Things

JAN WEEKS

Illustrated by Janine Dawson

sundance
A Haights Cross Communications Company

The Story Characters

Tim

Mandy

Mom

The Story Setting

TABLE OF CONTENTS

CHAPTER 1

Tim the Terror!

I have this little brother. His name is Tim. Mom wants me to like him, but I don't.

He takes all of my toys. Then he
breaks them into little pieces.

It all started when Tim was a baby. He couldn't talk, but he made loud "Give me!" noises.

"Waaaahhhhh!" he screamed, when he wanted one of my things.

When I didn't give it to him, he
screamed louder.

"Tim won't hurt it," Mom said. "Let him have a turn."

It was even worse when Tim learned to crawl. Down the hall he'd go on his fat, little hands and knees. Then he'd crawl straight into my bedroom.

CHAPTER 2

Find and Destroy!

One day, I found Tim sitting on my bedroom floor. He was chewing on my teddy bear's nose and drooling all over it.

Another day, he took my best doll. He pulled off one of its arms and most of its hair. When I took my doll back, he said it was his.

Tim yelled so loudly that Mom came running into the room.

"What have you done to him?" Mom asked me.

"Be nice to your little brother," she said as she cuddled Tim. "He's only a baby."

When Tim started to walk, things got
even worse. Nothing was safe. Not my
books! Not my toys! Not anything!

"He'll grow out of it," Mom said.

He didn't.

CHAPTER

Tim the Troublemaker

One day, Tim took my homework out of my schoolbag. He tore out all of the pages and ripped them into little pieces.

"I'm making snow!" he yelled. And he threw the pieces over his head.

So I didn't do my homework. My teacher was upset when I told her what Tim did to my homework. But she wasn't mad at Tim. She was upset with me.

"You must learn to be more careful, Mandy," she said. "Don't leave your things where your little brother can get them."

Where could that be?

I was getting really tired of Tim. I had to think of a way to keep him out of my bedroom.

A sign on the door that said **KEEP OUT TIM!** would not work. Tim couldn't read. I had to think of something else.

CHAPTER **4**

The Plan

Finally, I came up with a plan. I could hardly wait to try it out.

"I have a secret," I whispered into Tim's ear. Of course he wanted to know what it was.

"There is a hungry monster with sharp teeth living under my bed," I told him. "It's a great big, hairy monster that only eats little boys called Tim."

"Show me," Tim said. He began to drag me down the hall. Some kids don't know that you should be scared of monsters.

There was no monster under my bed. So I said, "Sh, he's sleeping. We'll come back later."

I had to think of a better plan.

Today I found Tim sitting in my bedroom again. He was drawing all over one of the school's brand-new library books.

"This is a picture of a house," he said, smiling at me. "I drew it just for you, Mandy."

"Now I'm going to get into big trouble with Mrs. Potts!" I yelled. "And she's the crankiest teacher in the school."

Tim put his arms around me. "I'm sorry, Mandy," he said, showing me his sorry face.

It was too late for that. I pushed him away. Then I told him to get out of my bedroom and stay out!

CHAPTER 5

The Better Plan

That afternoon, my friend Paul came over to my house.

Paul liked my new plan. "These golf balls make great eyes," he said.

We were sitting in my bedroom
making Mom's mop into a monster.

It was going to be Paul's job to hide
under the bed and be the monster.
When I brought Tim into the room,
Paul would roar.

When Tim got close enough, Paul the Monster was going to grab Tim's ankle and squeeze it.

It was a good plan, but it didn't work.

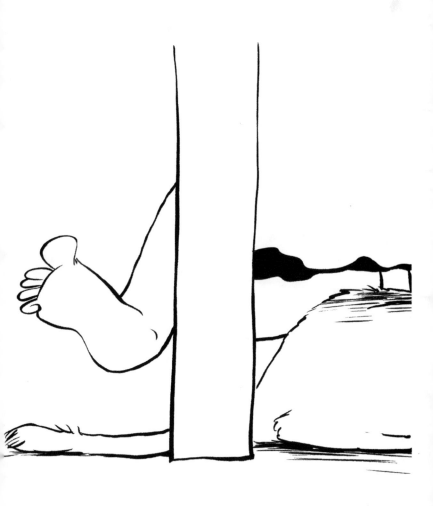

I didn't plan on the cat being asleep
under my bed. And I didn't plan on
Tim stepping on the cat's tail.

The cat let out such a screech that
I was the one who got scared.

As I jumped backward, I tripped over
the mop. I landed on the floor and
hurt my arm.

Now I've thought of a plan that's even better.

I'm going to ask Grandma if she would like Tim to live with her. I hope she says yes!

GLOSSARY

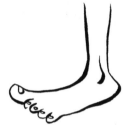

ankle
the joint where your foot meets your leg

crankiest
the angriest

cuddled
gave a big hug

destroy
wreck or break

terror
a big brat

upset
unhappy

worse
more than bad

Jan Weeks

Jan Weeks has written many poems, plays, songs, and stories for children. She is an experienced teacher with an interest in the development of sound reading skills and the promotion of literature. Jan is married and has three sons.

Janine Dawson

Janine loves to draw. In fact, she loves to draw a lot—and swim, but never at the same time. She lives with her daughter, two cats, and a nervous goldfish.

Published by Sundance Publishing
P.O. Box 1326, 234 Taylor Street, Littleton, MA 01460
800-343-8204

Copyright © text Jan Weeks
Copyright © illustrations Janine Dawson

First published 1999 as Sparklers by
Blake Education, Locked Bag 2022, Glebe 2037, Australia
Exclusive United States Distribution: Sundance Publishing

ISBN 0-7608-8004-2

Printed in Canada